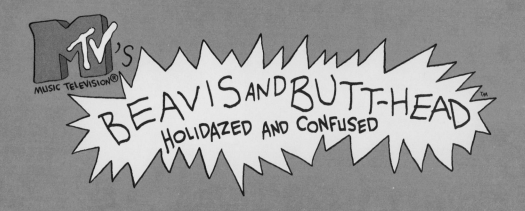

MTV's MUSIC TELEVISION® BEAVIS AND BUTT-HEAD™ HOLIDAZED AND CONFUSED

TELL OUR VIEWERS WHAT YOU HOPE TO ACCOMPLISH, SIR...

FOLKS, THE GOAL IS TO RAISE MONEY FOR OUR JUVENILE DELINQUENT RE-EDUCATION CENTER... AND IF WE CAN SCARE THE BEJEEZUS **INTO** SOME YOUNGSTERS, THAT'S JUST FROSTING ON THE BUN.

HOUSE OF SUCK

CHRISTIAN BUSINESSMEN'S ANNUAL
HAUNTED HOUSE
FOR CHARITY

BE BACK 5 MINUTES

HEY, BUTT-HEAD-- CHECK IT OUT... IT'S THAT DUDE **DRACLIA'S** HOUSE.

COOL! MAYBE HE'LL GIVE US, LIKE, SOME CANDY, OR SOME **BLOOD** OR SOMETHING...

UM, LIKE, GIVE US SOME **CANDY**, DRACLIA, AND WE WON'T STICK YOU WITH ONE'A THOSE **WOOD** THINGS.

HUH HUH HUH

KULL

BOYS, I GOT NO TIME FOR TOMFOOLERY... IT'S **TWO** BUCKS ADMISSION AND THE LINE STARTS OVER **THERE**...

SHORTLY...

DRACLIA SUCKS.

REALLY... IT'S, LIKE, NO MORE **MR. NICE DUDE**... LET'S GO IN THE BACK WAY AND DO SOME **TRICKS** OR SOMETHING.

THE BACK WAY

REAR ENTRY

PLEASE USE OTHER ORIFICE

YEAH! TRICKS **RULE**!

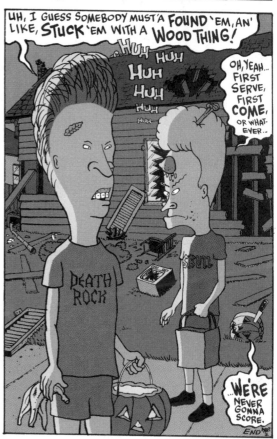

HA-HA! YOU'RE **BOTH** WRONG! I'M THE POOR TRAVELER SET UPON BY THIEVES ON HIS WAY TO JERICHO, LEFT IN THE DITCH AND ONLY LATER AIDED BY THE GOOD SAMARITAN !!!!

GOOD IDEA! **YOU** GIVE **US** YOUR CANDY... **WE'LL** LEAVE **YOU** IN A DITCH...

... THEN YOU CAN WAIT FOR THAT DUDE **SAM MARTIN** OR WHATEVER...

YOU KIDDER! I ALREADY BROUGHT **MY** CANDY HOME SO MY **MOM** CAN **RATION IT OUT** TO ME IN SMALL AMOUNTS OVER THE NEXT YEAR!

... YOU WUSS...

REALLY... I **NEVER** LET MY MOM **TOUCH** MY FOOD...

...WHO KNOWS WHERE **HER** HANDS HAVE BEEN ?!

LATER...

ENDORFFER

DING DONG! ≥HUH-HUH≤

...HOW TERRIFYING... BEAVIS, BUTT-HEAD, **AND** STEWART--**TOGETHER** AT MY HOUSE...

I'M **BEAVIS.** UH... ≥HEH-HEH≤

I'M **BUTT-HEAD.** KICK-OR-TREAT?

HI!

HURRY UP AND COME IN BEFORE THE **NEIGHBORS** SEE YOU...

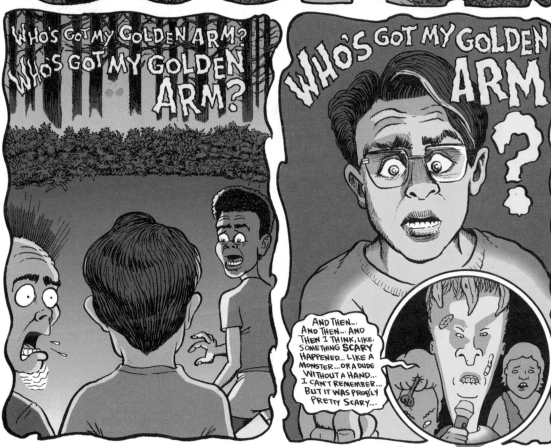

...OKAY... NOW IT'S **MY** TURN...

...ON A HALLOWEEN NIGHT, NOT SO LONG AGO, TWO BOYS THOUGHT IT WOULD BE COOL TO **SWITCH CLOTHES** AND GO OUT TRICK-OR TREATING DISGUISED AS EACH OTHER...

"...**ON** THAT VERY NIGHT **DEATH** CAME FOR ONE OF THE BOYS... BUT WHEN HE FOUND THEM, BECAUSE THEY HAD **SWITCHED CLOTHES,** HE COULDN'T TELL WHO WAS **WHO**...SO **DEATH** TOOK THEM **BOTH!!!**

"...**AND** TO THIS VERY DAY, THEY SIT WATCHING **TV** IN HELL, WHERE **EVERY SHOW SUCKS** AND THE ONLY MUSIC THEY CAN EVER LISTEN TO IS **OPERA**..."

THAT'S **STUPID.** IF DEATH TRIED TO GET **ME,** I'D KICK HIM IN TH' **NADS!**

YOU DUMBASS... DEATH DOESN'T **HAVE** ANY NADS, THEY FELL OFF WHEN HE DIED.

THEN GIMME MY SHIRT BACK, ASS-MUNCH! **I'M** NOT GOING DOWN TO **HELL** TILL I'M GOOD'N READY.

HUH-HUH "GOING DOWN."

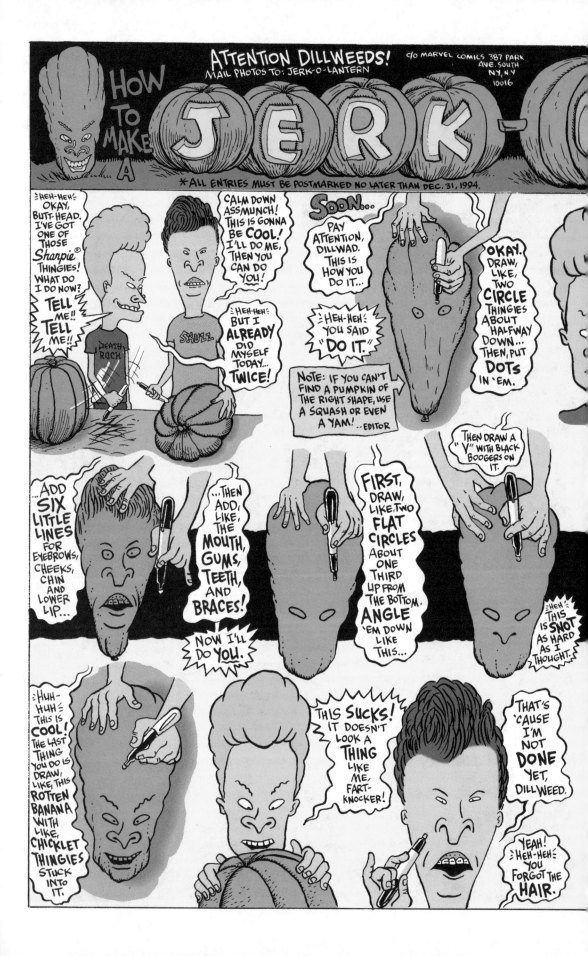

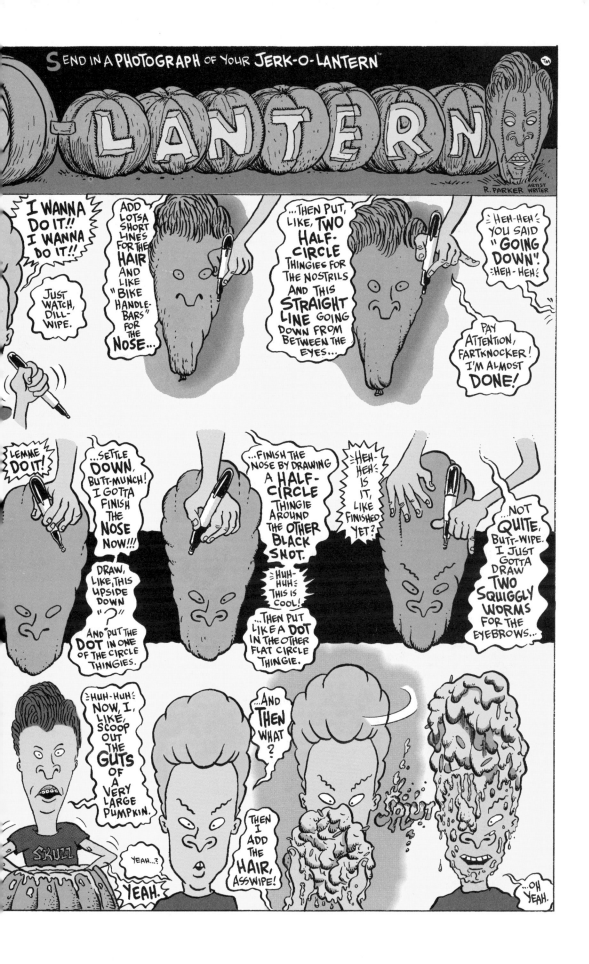

≥ HUH-HUH-HUH≤ CHECK IT **OUT**, BEAVIS! THAT'S WHAT CAN HAPPEN TO YOU IF YOU **"CHOKE YOUR CHICKEN"** TOO HARD.

OH, YEAH!! ≥ HEH-HEH≤ I **HATE** IT WHEN THAT HAPPENS.

THAT'S **RIGHT**, BOYS!

UH, WHUT?

IT **IS** TERRIBLE WHEN HELPLESS TURKEYS--OR **CHICKENS**, FOR THAT MATTER--GET NEEDLESSLY **CHOKED** AND SLAUGHTERED! THAT'S WHY I'VE DRESSED AS A DECAPITATED TURKEY... TO **PROTEST** THE CRUEL KILLING OF TURKEYS EVERY NOVEMBER...,

ARE YOU REALLY **"DECRAP**ITATED"?

...AN OTHERWISE **VERY** UPLIFTING HOLIDAY, ABOUT THE **FRIENDSHIP** BETWEEN THE EARLY SETTLERS AND THE **INDIANS**, AND ALSO ABOUT THE WONDERFUL **BOUNTY** OF THE **FALL HARVEST**, HAS BEEN **RUINED** BY THE BLOOD-THIRSTY FORCES OF ANTI-VEGETARIANISM...

...IT ALL BEGAN WHEN...

UH, WE, LIKE, GOTTA **GO**, OR SOMETHING.

YEAH! WE GOTTA GO TO THE BATHROOM TO **"DECRAPITATE"**.

BUT YOU CAN TELL US **MORE** LATER.

SHUT **UP**, DUMBASS!

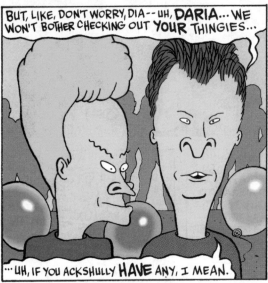

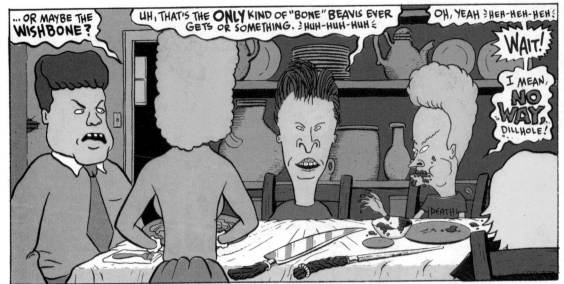

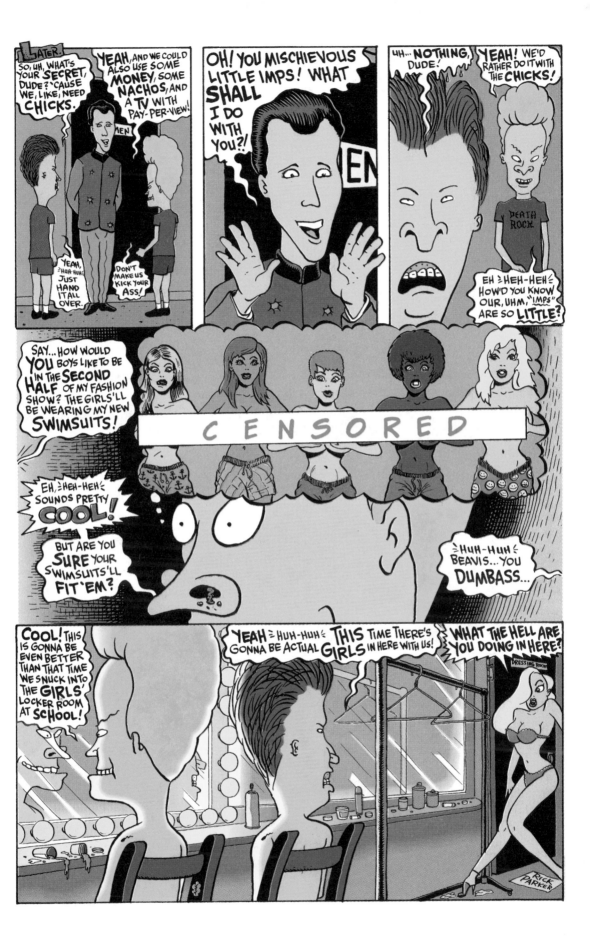

BY DUTTER, DANIELS AND CONRAD

SOONER... WHY, A CONDOM! HOW LOVELY...

LATER. COOL! YOU GOT MY GIFT!

THIS "CANDY" TASTES LIKE A GIANT WAD OF SNOT!

HEH-HEH! HE'S PRETTY SMART, BUTT-HEAD!

MUNCH MUNCH

I'M GONNA GIVE YOU PUNKS A CHRISTMAS GIFT YOU'LL NEVER FORGET!

COOL! I THOUGHT YOU WERE MAD AT US!

EARL-- WAIT--!!

YOU CAN'T BEAT UP SOMEONE ON SCHOOL GROUNDS--

...IT'S AGAINST THE RULES!

≥choke≤ IF... YOU... DIDN'T... ...HAVE ...ME... PINNED... AGAINST... THE WALL I'D BE... KICKING ...YOUR... ...ASS... ≥choke≤

THROTTLE

BEAVIS AND BUTT-HEAD! BECAUSE YOU HAVE BEEN DISRESPECTFUL TO THE FEELINGS OF OTHERS IN CHOOSING YOUR GRAB BAG GIFTS, I'M GOING TO HAVE TO GIVE YOU AN "F" FOR BEING INSENSITIVE...UNLESS....

≥choke≤ ...UNLESS... ...EARL... KICKS... ...OUR... ...ASS... INSTEAD...

NO!...UNLESS YOU GIVE ME AN ORAL REPORT ON THE TRUE MEANING OF CHRISTMAS!!

≥choke≤ ...I... THINK I'LL ...TAKE... ...THE ...ASS-KICKING...

WORDS: BARRY DUTTER
PICTURES: RON FRENZ &
AL MILGROM

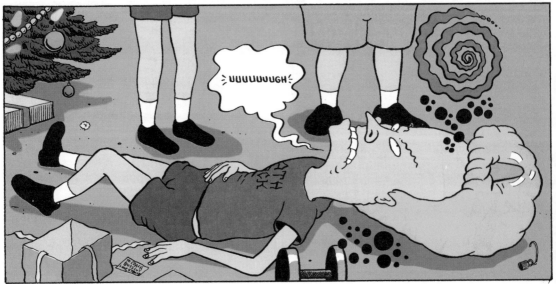

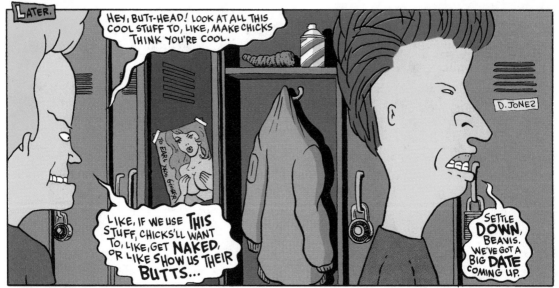

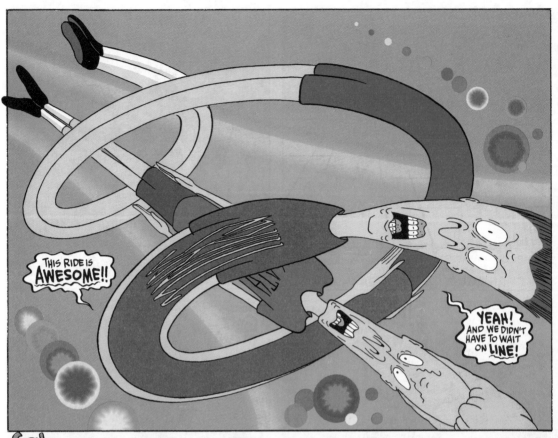

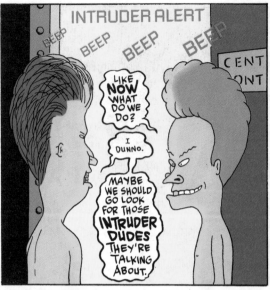